# Jesus in Nazareth

# Jesus in Nazareth

## Tales from his gap years

Tony Burnham

Matador
9 Priory Business Park,
Wistow Road, Kibworth Beauchamp,
Leicestershire. LE8 0RX
Tel: (+44) 116 279 2299
Fax: (+44) 116 279 2277
Email: books@troubador.co.uk
Web: www.troubador.co.uk/matador

ISBN 978 1788036 122

British Library Cataloguing in Publication Data.
A catalogue record for this book is available from the British Library.

Typeset in 11pt Minion Pro by Troubador Publishing Ltd, Leicester, UK

Matador is an imprint of Troubador Publishing Ltd

*For Hubert Cunliffe-Jones*
*1905-1991*
*theological college principal,*
*university professor and theologian*

# Contents

# Preface

This is a work of fiction. The Gospels leave an eighteen year gap in the story of Jesus. Luke tells of his visit as a twelve year old to the Temple in Jerusalem and then, apart from a couple of lines, there is nothing until his baptism by John, followed by the start of his public ministry when Jesus was about thirty years old.

What happened in those eighteen years? When Jesus began his ministry he cannot suddenly have become the person we know in the Gospels. Much must have happened to prepare him. We have some facts: Jesus lived and died; Nazareth was a hilltop village. There is tradition; for example, it is generally assumed that, as Joseph is not mentioned in Jesus' later life, he had died. Also there is all that historians now tell us about the political, economic and social contexts of the time and, in addition, work done by archaeologists. To this we can add some deductions from the Gospels and we can also use our imagination. While the Gospels give us the names of Jesus' four brothers, neither names nor number of sisters is given. I've assumed that there were two and I have named them. However the biblical foundation must be those words of Luke: 'And Jesus increased in wisdom and in years, and in divine and human favour'.

To give some unity to the various scenes, I've used the device of the old men of the village sitting in the shade of an ancient olive tree. One of them, a shepherd, is the village barber. Perhaps I should dedicate these pieces to all the Lancashire barbers in whose shops I've sat, waiting my turn. There I've listened to the banter and the crosstalk: football, politics, local gossip, jokes and, occasionally, religion.

These imagined scenes from the early life of Jesus are offered with the prayer of Martin Luther:

*'God, protect your Word against the preacher'.*

# Number 43

Jesus put down the draw knife and ran his fingers over the yoke he'd just finished. It was perfectly shaped to match the beast's neck, smooth so that it wouldn't chafe. Now, when it pulled the plough through the rough ground, it would be easier for the ox. He sighed. 'Perhaps I'd better visit the barber.'

Only that morning his mother had nagged him again about getting a haircut. 'After all', she said, 'you're nineteen and the head of our family so you need to look respectable.'

Jesus walked down the street to the ancient olive tree, where the old men sat in its shade, meeting for their daily parliament. Nazareth was only a small village with a population in hundreds, not thousands. Its houses were cut into the grey limestone hillside and everyone who was able had to work in the fields in the valley below – women as well as men. The old women stayed close to home, preparing the family's food. But the old men kept out of the way, often meeting each other under the tree. They were the heart of the village grapevine; they knew everyone and everything; they shared the gossip, both the trivia and the significant and, on a good day, you might even hear a wise word.

You often saw the barber there, cutting hair. It wasn't his main job. He was a shepherd, and a good one. He often said that the prophet Isaiah was his mentor. So he made sure his flock was fed and, if a lamb couldn't keep up, he'd carry it. But he was most skilled at shearing the sheep, cutting off the curled wool so carefully that they neither struggled nor bleated. And that's why the old men asked him to cut their hair. Though one of them said, 'I don't fancy those big shears close to my ear.' So he'd asked the blacksmith to make him a smaller pair and, ever since, he'd been known as "The Barber".

Jesus joined the group and sat a little distance from the old men. When his turn came, he sat on a tree stump and the barber began to cut and snip. He paused, waving his shears, 'Y'know, young man, your hair's longer than the mane on the head of a Nazarite. There was one here the other day, his father had died and he'd had to break his vows so he could care for the old man's body. And that meant the long hair he'd grown had to come off.'

'Maybe some men are called to serve God like that but it's not for me', said Jesus, 'God's less bothered about what's on the top of our heads than what goes on inside them.'

The barber continued to cut his thick black hair. 'You might well be right. But don't forget that hair's one of God's gifts. It keeps us cool when the day's hot and warm when the night's cold. And it's one way in which God knows us.'

'How do you mean?' asked Jesus.

The barber stood back for a moment and then he said, 'Here I am cutting the hair on your head but God will make each one grow again. Y'see, I think God knows us so well he's counted how many hairs we have; he numbers them.'

Before Jesus could reply, an old man joined the circle. He began unravelling the long scarf covering his head, revealing a pink bald pate. The other men began to laugh. One of them called out, 'I see you've come for your annual spit and polish'.

The newcomer looked straight back at him, 'God loves a bald man.' The old men laughed. So he went on, 'Don't forget, when the lads shouted at the prophet Elisha, "Baldy, Baldy", a couple of bears came out of the woods and mauled every one of them.' He shook his fist at them. 'Just you wait, with my bald head and trimmed beard the women'll look twice at me and then you'll be laughing the other side of your faces.'

Jesus brushed the loose hair off his shirt and then, touching his ear, he said to the barber, 'It's itching; I think you've missed one.'

The barber snipped it off, murmuring, 'It's Number 43'.

Jesus smiled, 'Number 43'.

# Fishing for Friends

It was a quiet day in the carpenter's workshop. With four brothers and a couple of sisters, Jesus had a big family to support and he was always glad to see customers. He never complained about being busy. Some of his work demanded great concentration as he carefully carved the wood into the right shape. But sometimes it was rather repetitive, requiring muscles rather than brains and then he could think while he worked. But it was a relief, occasionally, to have time for himself, especially when the blue sky and warm sun were so inviting. So he left his younger brother, James, in charge and went for a walk, breathing the fresh air and greeting old women sunning themselves by their open doors or passing children playing on the street.

He strolled down to the ancient olive tree, where the old men were sitting in the shade of its green leaves. They'd grown used to this serious young man joining them. It began with him bringing his elderly father, Joseph, to meet his old friends and Jesus would sit on the dry grass and watch the barber cutting their hair and trimming their beards, while he listened to the banter and smiled at their jokes. After Joseph died, he still came down and listened as they argued about politics and religion, discussing the weather and, their favourite subject, grumbling about the new teacher at the Synagogue – not as good as the last one. They never were.

Today, as he got nearer he could see that something different was happening. Talking to the old men was a couple of other young men. One was about his own age, nineteen or twenty. The other, a few years older, had a more weathered face and a voice that was a rough growl. On the floor was a large open basket, full of dried fish. The elder one was trying to persuade the old men to buy and the younger one was walking round showing them a very large one. 'We caught it and dried it ourselves.'

'Smells like it', and they all laughed. 'Still it's a good size', said the barber.

'Good size' repeated the offended fisherman, 'why this could have been the fish that swallowed Jonah.'

'Come on', said his brother to the old men, 'you can trust us, everyone in Capernaum knows Simon and Andrew'.

At this, Old Grumpy muttered loudly. 'A bunch of rogues down there.'     Realising that he wasn't getting anywhere the older brother eyed Jesus. He looked a soft touch, so he said to Andrew, 'Show that beauty to the young chap over there'. And he called out: 'It's a bargain, Sir. Stick a gold coin in its mouth and it's yours.'

Jesus laughed, 'It'd certainly feed my family but Nazareth's a poor village. You'd be better going to Sepphoris; that's where the money is.'

'Sepphoris? That's a joke, a city full of Greeks and you know what they're like. They'd fry the fish and skin us.'

'At least you'd get some money, there's none here. Why bother with us?'

The quieter brother looked miserable. 'We owe money for tax and the steering oar on our boat broke up in a storm. We had to cast our nets from the shore to catch these. Y'see, in Capernaum, our regular customers only pay us enough to support our families. So we thought we'd come and see if the kind folk of Nazareth would like our fish and then we could make some extra.'

'You'll not find any spare money here,' said Jesus, 'I'll tell you what; leave your basket and the fish and we'll share it out as our families need. And, in return, the barber'll cut your hair and I'll come and fix your boat.'

'That's a good offer Simon,' said Andrew to his brother. But Simon only pointed at Jesus and laughed, 'He could no more fix our boat than my mother-in-law could.'

At that, Alphaeus shouted out, 'Watch your mouth young man. Jesus is the best carpenter in the district. He's just made me a yoke for our ox that was so comfortable I could have worn it and pulled the plough myself.'

On their way home, Andrew asked Simon why he'd changed his mind.

'I'm not sure; I can't explain it. There was something about him – reliable….. no, it was more than that. He seemed a good man; and it was the way the old men trusted somebody so young. Another thing, Andrew, I didn't change my mind, somehow he did that.'

# The Miracle of Healing

Some of the old men, who sat under the ancient olive tree in Nazareth, were playing a game of five stones, using the knuckle bones from sheep. Others lazily watched and contented themselves by passing on the latest gossip. But most, lulled by the heat of the sun, the clickety-click of the bones and the buzz of flies, gave up and took a nap. So when one old chap rushed up, almost tripping over his stick in agitation, saying, 'You'll never guess what I've seen', they all sat up sharply, waiting for the details. 'Come on,' said one eagerly, 'Let's hear it.'

'I've just seen young Jesus with a girl.' Their eyes popped because that didn't seem like Jesus. He was so earnest, almost a bit too good for his age. Even so, he was probably the most eligible young man in the village; head of his family and a skilled craftsman. True, when it came to looks, he wasn't any different from other young men of his age – average height, dark hair and beard, olive skin. You wouldn't pick him out in a crowd, unless you were close enough to see his eyes, brown and sharp. His gaze could cut to your heart as easily as his axe split wood, unless it was accompanied by his slow smile. A good man, who everyone thought would make a fine loving husband.

The old men thought this was great news – 'A girl, a girl?' They turned to each other in excitement. 'It's about time', said Alphaeus. 'You should hear what Mary has to say on the subject'.

'Who was the girl?'

'I couldn't see; her face was veiled'.

The barber shook his head at their foolishness. 'Since Joseph died, Jesus hasn't been able to think about marrying. With his family to support, his building work and the time he spends studying the scriptures, he's better things to do than looking for a wife. Anyway you're making a fuss over nothing. It'll be one of his sisters'. And he was proved right when Jesus arrived, bringing Naomi because she had a pain and was unable to sleep.

The barber didn't only keep sheep and cut hair. He also knew about sickness and healing. As he used to say, 'You can't be a good shepherd without knowing how to keep the flock healthy'. He sat Naomi down on the tree stump and she looked at the ground, embarrassed at being watched by all the old men.

'She has toothache', said Jesus.

The barber raised her chin and asked her to lift her veil. The pain was obvious in her pale face with, on one side, a bright red patch. The barber stroked it and she jerked back.

'Show him', said Jesus and she opened her mouth so that the barber could see the abscess, raw and fiery.

He reached for his cloth bag and pulled out a small flask, its opening stuffed with a rag. He shook the flask, pulled out the rag and it dripped violet. 'I use it on the lambs, when their gums are sore from suckling. It's alright, it won't hurt, it's the juice of a flower', and he dabbed her swollen gum. 'I'll give some to your brother and your mother can dab it on morning and night. And there's something else, which will help. You'll need some of the strong spirit we make at the harvest from grapes' skin. When at night you lie on your bed, swill it round and round your mouth. And as you wash your mouth with the spirit, sing to yourself a Psalm:

"*When I call, answer me God.*

*In my distress ........take pity on me and hear my prayer.*

*In peace I lie down and at once fall asleep,*

*for it is you and none other, Lord, who make me rest secure.*" '

Naomi smiled her gratitude to the barber before covering her face again.

'Thank you', said Jesus.

'No', replied the barber, 'thank God for the miracle of healing.'

# A Pharisee for the Synagogue

Jesus yawned. It had been a rough night. The younger members of the family wouldn't go to sleep. They argued about which story they wanted to be told by their mother. The girls wanted to hear about the baby in the rushes; about Moses' sister, Miriam, and the Egyptian Princess. The boys wanted the stories of Moses and Aaron confronting the Pharaoh. How Aaron's staff turned into a snake and Egypt's rivers and lakes changed into blood. Jesus, tired after a hard day in the workshop, turned over and covered his head with his robe. He didn't want to hear, yet again, about plagues of frogs, gnats, flies and festering boils.

For such a big family, it was only a small house cut into the rock and then extended outside. Underneath was an enclosed space to shelter their donkey and a few sheep overnight. Mary and the girls cooked in the yard. The living area was not much more than one big room split by a few curtains. Jesus had to share a bed with one of his brothers. But, hearing the hum of Mary's voice, as her stories quietened the younger ones, he was soon asleep. Then suddenly James' sharp elbow cracked against his rib. 'Sorry. Was I snoring?' he mumbled.

'Listen,' whispered James. There was a soft knocking against the outer door. 'There's someone there.'

Reluctantly, Jesus rolled out of bed and tip-toed in the darkness to the door. Knock....Knock. He opened it and peered out, 'Who's there?'

'It's me, Clopas.' It was the husband of Mary's friend. 'Travellers have arrived and we've no fresh food left. Have you any to spare?'

It was a long time before Jesus got back to sleep. That was why, in the morning, he yawned. It was then he remembered that the new teacher at the synagogue was going to meet some of Nazareth's old men. The barber had suggested that Jesus ought to be there, 'The old men might be upset because he's a Pharisee and they're not used to them.'

When the Teacher arrived, the barber suggested that he sit on the tree stump. 'You're going to cut his hair then?' called out one of them. The barber glared at him.

The Teacher was quite an imposing figure in his long robe with tassels at the corners of its fringes. He also had a small box of texts strapped to his forehead. The old men gawped. Then, to their astonishment, he said, 'I hope that some of you are going to buy my pots.'

It was a while since they'd had a potter living in the village and so they murmured with pleasure. Until Old Grumpy asked, 'I suppose all the bowls will have little tassels dangling from their sides?' That silenced them, so Jesus laughed, 'Pay no attention. Nazarenes always welcome newcomers by being rude to them.'

'And these old men are the rudest,' added the barber.

The Teacher smiled, 'You can guess what my father said the first time he saw me wearing these tassels. But it's the Law of Moses. They're to remind me to obey the Commandments.'

'Well, what about that little box on your forehead? Is that where you keep your....'

The barber interrupted. 'Show some respect. Your trouble is you don't know the scriptures well enough. There are words in that box that tell of the Lord bringing our people out of Egypt. Isn't that so Teacher?'

'That's right. It's to remind us to praise God for setting us free from slavery.'

Old Grumpy, determined to have the last word, turned on Jesus. 'You're a pious young man, why don't you wear bits dangling from your robe and put a box on your forehead?'

'You know what carpenters are like – if we had a box there, we'd keep nails in it.' And then Jesus became serious. 'We should keep the Law in our hearts and the praise of God on our lips. But I don't disagree with our Teacher. It doesn't matter how we remind ourselves, as long as we live by the Law.'

In that spirit, the conversation continued until the Pharisee stood, 'You know where to find me. If I'm not in the synagogue, I'll be shaping the clay into water jars and pots.'

The barber couldn't resist, 'That reminds me of my favourite prophet, Isaiah. He said that we are the clay and God is our potter.'

The Teacher had made a friend.

# A Wedding at Nazareth

'It's ridiculous', groused Old Grumpy to his friends sitting in the shade of the ancient olive tree, as they watched the barber at work. 'Everyone's bothering the barber on the same day'.

'Well you know what weddings are like', said Jesus. 'We all want our hair tidied and beards trimmed. And this wedding's a big one. With so many guests coming from Capernaum, we don't want them to think Nazarenes are scruffy.'

One of them, keeping a straight face, turned to Jesus. 'It's not your wedding then?'

He smiled. 'You're as bad as my mother. She's always nagging me about finding a nice girl. But you know Mary – who'd be good enough for her? Besides, I've work to do for God. But until I know what that is, I'm better staying single.'

The barber stopped cutting and looked round: 'Leave him alone. He's enough on his plate with four brothers, not to mention his sisters and Mary. And look how he keeps an eye on us.' He waved his shears, 'My guess is that when he knows what God wants him to do, you see, he'll have an even larger family to worry about.' And he clicked his shears and turned back to finish trimming a beard.

The celebrations began. It was the best time of the year. The harvest had been gathered, the grapes had been trod and the wine stored in new skins. The season's hard work was done. Now evenings were pleasant, neither too hot nor too cold. Everyone could sit around outside and relax. It was the perfect time for a wedding and, usually, the whole village would join in. The musicians would get out their flutes and strings and the younger folk would pick up their tambourines and dance. Everyone would join in the singing, especially when they were from The Song of Songs. A favourite was the Song of the Bridegroom:

> *My dove, that hides in holes in the cliffs*
> *or in crannies on the terraced hillside,*
> *let me see your face and hear your voice;*
> *for your voice is sweet, your face is lovely.*

As the bride and groom were from different places, the two communities began by sitting apart. Then Jesus saw his friends, Simon and Andrew. 'I see that Capernaum comes to Nazareth again. I hope it doesn't mean you've broken the oar I made. Are you still steering straight?'

'Oh yes, we're the envy of all the fishermen', said Simon. 'You ought to go out with us on the lake sometime. You might even get some more business. But come and meet Zebedee's lads, James and John.'

'Not more fishermen!' said Jesus.

Zebedee's James sighed and turned to Simon, 'You know what they say, "Can any good thing come out of Nazareth?" '

14

His brother elbowed him and, winking at Jesus, went on 'Behave yourself, we're guests here. Watch what you say or they'll be serving you some of their best vinegar'.

'So you're John. They've told me you're a good chap', said Jesus. 'I can see we both share the same problem; we've each got a brother called James. And they too have something in common; they're both troublemakers. I'd like you to meet my mother. She'll be pleased to see that not all my friends are ruffians.'

Just then there was a shout, 'It's the bridegroom'. The musicians struck up a tune and everyone stood to watch the bridesmaids take their lamps and go out to welcome him and bring him in to meet the bride. As the bridegroom took the bride's hand, Jesus looked round at his friends, 'Let's praise God with some words of Isaiah "As the bridegroom rejoices over the bride, so shall God rejoice over you." '

'I'll drink to that', said Simon. 'And the food looks good, let's eat.'

There was lamb from the hills, fish from the Sea of Galilee and bread in freshly baked loaves. The four fishermen and the carpenter, ate and drank, talked and laughed. And the wine flowed.

Simon raised his cup, 'A toast – to this wine – at least one good thing comes out of Nazareth'.

'I'm glad you've noticed', said Jesus, 'and let's thank God that, after all these years not knowing each other, now we've found real friendship.'

'I'll say this about you Nazareth folk', said Simon, 'you save the best wine to the end.'

# The Lost Lamb

Every evening, when most folk were at home, preparing to eat, a woman, dressed in black, walked swiftly up the street in Nazareth. Her head was bent low; she looked neither to the right nor to the left until she reached the synagogue. Half an hour later, she returned. And every evening, the old men, in their regular place under the ancient olive tree, sent there by wives and daughters to be out of their way until supper was ready, watched her come up the street and later return down it.

Sharing the gossip, as old men like to do, they had pieced together her story. The fact that she no longer wore a veil meant that she was neither a wife nor a daughter but a widow. They could see that, compared with their ages, she was still young, in her mid-twenties. She was from nearby Magdala. As they'd so many Marys in Nazareth, the old men called her, "Magdalene" after her town. There she'd been the wife of a much older man, a rich merchant. Magdala was on the trade route from Damascus to the Mediterranean coast and was a busy place, full of people from many different nations. Caravans halted there, buying provisions, trading their goods.

The rough camel drivers liked to spend the night on the town and it was not easy living there when you were a single woman. Within the settled community, her husband had been particularly despised because, although he was a Jew, he had numerous business dealings with Gentiles. When he died, not only did his wealth pass to Mary but so did the shame. Because of this she had left Magdala and moved to the countryside and had settled in the more sedate and safe village of Nazareth.

One evening, Jesus came to the tree and asked where the barber was? The old men liked nothing better than to pull Jesus' leg. 'There must be a girl involved if you want your beard trimming again.'

Jesus was growing more and more irritated by their silly jokes. He liked to laugh but their frequent mention that it was time he was married was going too far. It's true that most young men of his age were already married, some had children. Parents arranged husbands and wives for their daughters and sons when they were much younger than nineteen. But Jesus was different;

He had the same desires as young men and he liked the company of women. But he'd resisted all attempts to settle him. Partly it was that he'd had to take the place of Joseph and help his mother look after the other children and, most seriously, he burned with an inner conviction that God had something special planned for him. He was glad that his mother agreed. She used to say that one day 'he'd be a sign' to people and that, like Hannah with her son Samuel, she would 'make him over to the Lord'.

Jesus swallowed his irritation, 'I know that "a good wife is a great blessing", – though you wouldn't think so from the hours you spend under this tree away from yours. No, I don't want a trim; I've just brought back the oil the barber gave me for my sister's toothache.'

Alphaeus was shamed by Jesus' reproach. 'The barber's not come back from his sheep yet. You know what he's like. When he counted them into the fold, one was missing. So he's been out all day on the hills searching for this one little lost lamb.'

One of them, seeing the widow coming up the road, muttered to his neighbour, 'Here's the Magdalene; I don't care what he says, she's pious enough for him and wealthy with it. They'd make a grand couple.'

Jesus watched as the young widow passed them on her way to the synagogue, dressed in black from top to toe, her head bent low, and looking neither to the right nor the left.

Then someone shouted, 'The barber's back.' And he appeared, dishevelled and tired. But across his shoulders was the lost lamb and, on his face, a big smile.

'That's what the Magdalene needs', thought Jesus, 'a good shepherd.'

# All at Sea

Jesus loaded the basket with some tools and hung it on the side of the donkey. 'While I'm away James look after the family and the workshop.' James was Mary and Joseph's second son. Altogether they'd had five boys, as well as their girls. Since Joseph's death, Jesus had been kept busy making sure that they all had enough to eat. It wasn't easy for a nineteen year old and Nazareth was only a big village. Now he was going to the nearby town of Capernaum to earn extra money. He could have made more by going to Sepphoris. It was nearer and there was plenty of building work. But it was a Greek city and he preferred the country areas and his own folk.

He passed the old men sitting under the ancient olive tree and one called out, 'Where are you off to now?'

'To the Sea of Galilee; Simon and Andrew say that there's work for me repairing some fishing boats.'

'See that you bring us back some fish. And make sure it's fresh.'

Jesus had first met the two brothers when they'd come to Nazareth selling their fish. Later he'd visited them to fix their boat and now they'd sent him a message that there was more work for a good carpenter.

After some days' hard work, when Jesus had pieced new planks into hulls, shaped oars, even made a new mast and the yard from which the sail hung, Simon came by. 'Why not go fishing with us tonight? That'll show you what real work's like.'

Jesus looked hesitant. He had never been out on the water. Like most of his people, he associated the sea with evil. He knew that, even before God had made the earth and its people, there was nothing but 'darkness over the face of the deep'. The scriptures had even hinted that storms were caused by great monsters, Leviathans, thrashing about in the depths. The sea was dangerous and dark. Jesus felt queasy at the thought of a night on the waves.

'I thought you trusted God,' said Simon. 'Have you forgotten the Lord dried up the sea to let our people escape the Egyptians? Anyway you eat the fish that swim there, so come with us and help us catch some.'

Simon, Andrew and their men pushed out the flat-bottomed boat and helped Jesus in. He flopped on a seat across the stern. 'Not there,' said Simon. 'We don't have passengers on this boat.' He handed Jesus an oar and helped him move carefully to one of the oarsmen's seats. Then they set off from the shore.

Jesus didn't last long. His oar caught crabs and splashed the other men. His face showed the ache of exerting different muscles from the ones he used as a carpenter. To his relief, Andrew called out, 'The water's calm. Why don't you let Jesus steer?'

'He'll only take us on to the rocks, to make more work for himself,' said Simon. But then he showed Jesus how to use the steering oar, which was pivoted on one side of the boat. Whoever steered had to stand on the keel, which wasn't easy even in a calm sea. The four oarsmen sat facing him, with their backs to the prow. So the steersman not only had to take the boat in the right direction, using the currents and avoiding the big waves, he also had to keep his eyes on the water, watching for disturbances on the surface that revealed a shoal.

Simon steadied him, making sure Jesus didn't fall overboard. 'I don't want you sinking the boat.'

Suddenly Jesus shouted with excitement, 'Look, over there, some fish, throw the nets over that side.'

'He's right,' Simon called to the others, 'Put the nets over the side and praise God for our supper.' He turned to Jesus, 'We'll make a fisherman of you yet.'

Some days later, it was nearly dark when the donkey plodded back into Nazareth. The barber was sitting with a few friends under the olive tree, 'Glad to see you back, Jesus.'

'You will be when you see what's in my basket for you all. The boys have sent some fish. They said it might stop you being rude about Capernaum.' Jesus dug his heels into the sides of the donkey and shouted, 'And I caught them.'

# A Day Out

The children ran part way up the hillside and then rolled over and over down to the bottom. After the hot season, the rain had fallen and, as if by magic, spikes of new growth pushed through the earth, scenting the air with the fresh green grass. As far as they could see, it was dotted with flowers.

Mary had told Jesus that she needed a bit of peace so would he take the livelier younger ones out for a walk. 'Tire them out', she said, 'I just need a few hours quiet'. So he'd left James in charge of the workshop and, with the four younger ones, had started to climb the hill into the surrounding countryside.

Miriam was the youngest and, at first, didn't join in the noisy games of her sister and brothers but stayed close to her eldest brother. He sat watching them play, chewing a blade of fresh grass. She climbed on his lap and took one of his hands between hers, feeling its roughness, calloused from working with coarse hewn wood and stone. She looked into his eyes.

Jesus smiled at her and then continued watching the others, who were now playing tig. Suddenly Miriam asked, 'Why did Dadda die?'

'D'you remember him?' It had now been about five years

since Joseph had died. Miriam had only been two or three at the time but she replied, 'I liked him. He always smelt of sawdust.'

Jesus laughed, 'That's because he was a clever carpenter and he worked hard. He never stopped thinking of Mamma and the rest of us.......' She interrupted, 'So why did he go and die?' 'Well, he was older than Mamma when they married and then they had our big family to love – feeding and clothing us. That meant that he had to work long hours. Sometimes he had to travel to earn extra money. Then, when he returned home, he couldn't rest but had to spend time with us. He wanted to be sure that we learned about God's love. One day he was so tired that he went to sleep and didn't wake up.'

Miriam listened carefully and then asked, 'If I have to work hard, will I die?' By this time, Simon, who was a couple of years older than Miriam, had realised he might be missing something and had come over. He heard Jesus say, 'We all die some day but you'll live for many years yet.' 'That's right', said Simon, 'And don't forget to tell her about resurrection.'

'How do you know?' asked Jesus.

'Teacher told us – about Enoch, walking with God and then God took him away. He didn't die.' As he ran off to rejoin the others, he shouted, 'Elijah was the same'.

'Ah, the new Teacher belongs to the Pharisees and they believe that, at the end of time, all who trust God will live.'

'So we'll see Dadda again?'

'I hope so', said Jesus. 'But the place where we can see him now is in our lives. We're his children and he lives on in us'.

'But I'm a girl.'

'That doesn't matter; we learned from him not to be selfish and to love each other. When we do that, we remind each other of him.' They sat quietly for a while. 'He also taught us that we didn't only have to look after ourselves. We've also to care for the poor.'

'Like Mamma does', said Miriam.

'Yes, like Mamma – and now she wants you to play, so off you go.'

Jesus sat silently and, closing his eyes, remembered Joseph's patience when he taught him how to choose the right piece of wood for a job; how to cut and shape it; how, when he was younger and had been naughty, after reproving him, Joseph had not been too hard on him. A merciful man – that was Joseph. It was Joseph's goodness which had taught him that God was like a loving father.

As they walked home, Jesus told them to listen for the birds – 'God cares for them'. They collected flowers and smelled them –'They're another of God's gifts. Look at how the fields are covered with grass. Isn't God good? But it's not only God who works; we have to help. If God's going to feed us, we must sow the seeds, mill the grain and bake the bread.' The children hopped and skipped following the path home. 'Look', Jesus called out, 'd'you see that bee? If we follow it, we might find some honey to take back for Mamma and the others.'

As they approached the village, Miriam put her hand in Jesus' and looked up at him. 'You smell of sawdust. Will you be my Dadda now?'

# My Friend the Tax Collector

Building a house took stone, some timber, mud and dung plastered on the outside and, for the roof, a few planks laid across the walls, covered with mats and packed tight with clay. There was plenty of stone in Nazareth but the house Jesus was building was only half-finished and he didn't want to run out of wood. He took the donkey and set off to Capernaum, where he knew he'd be able to buy more. While he was there, he called at the Custom House to see his friend, the tax collector.

Although Levi was a few years older than Jesus, they'd grown up together. They were the cleverest lads of their generation. Jesus was the thinker and Levi the one good with numbers. But Levi had become very unpopular by working as a customs officer for the Romans. Many of the tax collectors were greedy but because Levi did not defraud people, he and Jesus had stayed friends.

Levi offered him a bed for the night and so, after Jesus had bought the timber and Levi's duties for the day were done, they had a leisurely supper and caught up with each other's news. Their conversation followed the usual path: Levi inquired about Alphaeus, his father, and about his mother and James, his older brother. The latter was an extremely patriotic Jew and it was thought that he was a member of the Zealots. The Romans treated them as terrorists and, if they were caught, they risked being crucified. 'But you know me, Jesus', said Levi. 'I'm a patriot too. What other job could I do? I'm useless with my hands; I couldn't be a farmer like James. God's given me a head for figures. When the merchants pass through the gate, I can quickly estimate the value of their goods and calculate the tax. But I don't cheat them; I let the poor slip through without paying and I even turn a blind eye to passing Zealots. I admit I'm colluding with our people's enemies. But it must be better for tolls to be collected by someone who helps his own people, rather than by someone who exploits us.'

Jesus looked him in the eye. 'You're not telling me that you're satisfied with living like this. Being a good Jew isn't only about favouring our own people. Is this the best way to love our Father in heaven?'

Levi shook his head sadly. 'I know – but I still fast and tithe even if I can't go to Synagogue. Every Sabbath I long to worship there but folk won't have me. Most of all, I wish I was back with the family. When you see my father and mother, tell them I think of them every day; James as well', adding wistfully, 'We used to get on so well together when we were boys.'

The next morning Jesus set off for home, his donkey

loaded with wood. When he reached Nazareth, he passed the old men, sitting under the ancient olive tree, and he called out: 'Has anyone seen Alpheus?'

'Who's asking?' came the sullen reply from Old Grumpy. 'Not that renegade Levi.'

'He's not all bad', said Jesus. 'He's clever, kind-hearted and generous. He loves God. We need people like him in Nazareth. He's so many talents that I'd like to change his name to "Matthew" – the gift of God.'

'You're too soft. If I could get hold of him, I'd take the barber's shears and give him such a haircut, he'd never need another. I don't know why you waste your time with him.'

'Because Levi could be even better,' said Jesus. 'He could be a really good man. But if I spent my time with you, it would be wasted.'

Old Grumpy bridled, 'What d'you mean?'

Jesus smiled, 'Well we all know you're good enough already.' The leaves on the ancient olive tree shook with the old men's laughter. It was the joke of the day.

The barber stopped cutting, 'Him, good?' He looked round at the men, and, pointing at Jesus with his shears said, 'There's only one of us here who's good.' He shook his head at their stupidity and returned to his cutting.

Jesus walked on, rubbed the donkey's ear and whispered, 'Only God's good, only God.'

# A Nazareth Sabbath

The synagogue wasn't just a place for worship; it was the people's meeting room in Nazareth. It was a place of study, for argument and debate. Jesus and his friends were schooled there. But on the Sabbath it was where the people worshipped God. Afterwards, it emptied slowly. They'd praised God, singing psalms and praying. They'd seen the Teacher take out a precious scroll and heard him read and explain God's word.

Inside men and boys sat together, separate from the women and the girls. But outside, families came together again. Boys eyed the girls; and girls, the boys. Although Jesus was only a young man, since Joseph died he'd been head of the family, though wise enough to defer to Mary. While his four brothers talked to their friends, Jesus stood by his mother, keeping an eye on his sisters who waited demurely next to her.

The other young men were hesitant about approaching Jesus. He was so clever that they were in awe of him. In class, he'd even taken on their teacher in argument. But the young unmarried women kept glancing in his direction; their mothers too. He may not have looked particularly handsome but he was a skilled craftsman and worked hard; he was a family man. But there was something else about him. Mary the Magdalene had said it one day when the women talked as they washed their clothes in the pool. She said, 'He's special, different, the word that comes to me is "holy". ' They all agreed that he'd make a fine husband.

For friends Jesus had come to rely on some hardworking fishermen from the next town, as well as Levi the tax collector, shunned by everyone else.

Mary turned to him: 'I think we should invite the barber to share our supper. It must be lonely being a widower without any children. And there's also Widow Mary, the Magdalene. You go and invite him and I'll ask her.'

It had been tiring standing in the synagogue and so when the service was over, the old men had hobbled out to sit in the shade of the ancient olive tree, where they began their weekly inquest on the sermon. They were soon deep into friendly bickering. But, when they saw Jesus coming, one of them said, 'Young Jesus'll soon put us right and settle the argument.' And they waved him over.

The most vociferous old man began, 'A pious young man like you must agree with our Teacher when he says that we must obey the Commandment about the Sabbath, that it's a day of rest, even for our livestock. So I want to know how the barber can stop his sheep cropping the grass on the Sabbath. They're working. They're growing wool and getting fat with meat.' They all laughed.

'You can't expect dumb animals to understand the

Commandments when wise old men like you are bemused by them. Perhaps,' Jesus added slyly, 'even such holy men as yourselves disobey the commandments occasionally.'

'Cheeky young man', said Old Grumpy.

'Maybe the Teacher won't agree with me but, more and more, I'm beginning to think that not every part of the Law is equal.'

'What d'you mean? asked the barber.

'Well some Commandments are about being obedient to God and living a good life and caring for our neighbour. They're about loving-kindness, justice and mercy. But others are part of our ritual, like the Laws on the Sabbath and rules about cleanliness. They have a place but are less important. D'you remember that Sabbath when that ox of Clopas got stuck over the cliff edge and we had to get ropes and struggle to lift it back on to the field? We broke the Law then. On that occasion, working on the Sabbath was doing a good deed for our neighbour.'

'Good for the ox, as well,' said the barber. And they all laughed.

'That's what I mean – the Law's about loving God by loving our neighbour, especially if they're in need. I'm sure God preferred us to save that beast rather than sacrifice it in the Temple.'

Jesus spoke quietly to the barber, 'Mary says come round for supper'.

'Alright, I'll be glad to, but I'd better wait until after the sun's gone down.'

# To the Hills

The two young men left Nazareth and began to walk up the hillside. A few trees gave way to flowering shrubs, attracting the insects and giving off the scent of sage. There was a verse of the prophet Isaiah they both liked to sing:

*'You will go out with joy and be led forth in peace.*
*Before you mountains and hills will break*
*into cries of joy,*
*and all the trees in the countryside will*
*clap their hands.'*

They came to a sheepfold and sat with their backs against its wall and looked back down the hill they'd climbed. The weather was hot. Too hot. Everywhere was dry and dusty; brown grass and drooping plants. The higher they'd climbed, the cooler it became and, in the shade of the wall, the heat was bearable. 'You have to get above Nazareth to see it best,' said Jesus. 'You can't hide a town built on a hilltop. I suppose it was chosen because it would be easier to protect from an enemy.'

'Nazareth's only a village, not worth defending', said John. He was used to Jerusalem, where his father took his turn serving in the Temple. Their mothers were relatives and John was only six months older than Jesus. 'Is this the sheepfold you've to repair?'

Jesus stood and looked at the walls. 'Some of these stones need to be re-laid. I can see the main job's to fix the entrance; make a new gate.' He'd just got out his measuring line, when the shepherd came down the hill. 'I've brought John; his mother's a relation of Mary', said Jesus. 'I thought it would do him good, he's more used to city life than fields.'

'I thought we were meeting a barber', said John.

Jesus and the shepherd laughed. 'They call me that because I cut hair as slickly as I shear my sheep. But these animals are my real work.'

'True', said Jesus 'I think he loves his lambs more than people.'

'I'm not surprised', said John. 'The way folk live now is a disgrace. They neglect the Commandments and they need to repent.'

'It's not that', said the barber, picking up a lamb. 'When you've helped the ewe give birth, and seen the lamb staggering onto its feet and then being suckled by its mother, you feel for them and want to keep them safe. I suppose I'm soft but I give them all names and, when I shout, they recognise me. Now that's how God thinks of us.' He stroked the lamb's head. 'When you were climbing up, did you see the holes of the foxes' dens? Well, if you climb higher, there are wolves lurking. That's why I need a new gate. I can't lie across the door of the fold to keep them out all the time.'

Jesus smiled at John, 'We think of him as the barber, but really, he's a good shepherd'.

John sighed, 'It may be dangerous out here for us and for the sheep but I think I could settle for such a life. I'm tired of the city. You'd be disgusted at some of the goings on. The last Herod was bad enough, marrying ten wives, murdering some of them and a few of his sons. But I'm not sure his son Antipas is any better. I've heard that he's now infatuated with his niece and she's already the wife of his brother. D'you wonder why ordinary folk are as they are? Religion's got to be simpler and more disciplined. I say bring back the true piety of the Commandments and the justice they promise to all who keep the Law.' John sat up, 'You know what I'd like to do? I'd like to bring people out into this fresh air, wash them clean in the River Jordan, cross over it again. Then I'd teach them how to find a purer life in the desert.'

The barber, always practical, looked at the enthusiastic young man, 'Even if you're right, what would you live on out here?'

'Oh there are plenty of locusts; I've seen nuts and berries on the bushes. Bees would give honey and there's milk from the sheep and wild goats', replied John.

Jesus grasped John's shoulder and levered himself up, 'You may be right but I've a job to do. I want to measure that gate. Back in the workshop I've a big stone that someone chipped. It'd make a good cornerstone.'

John lay down, pillowing his hands behind his head. That's a good idea. I'll go on dreaming but I'll leave the foundations to you.'

# The Nazareth Caravan

The smell of smouldering wood from the early morning fires seeped into the cold air. It was still too dark to see anything. The sound of slithering feet came from the paths down the hillside, as those going to the Temple stumbled down to the meeting place, by the ancient olive tree.

Jerusalem was 80 miles distant and a journey lasting several days meant an early start. It was better to travel in a group as they would be passing through bandit country. Not that Nazareth folk had anything worth stealing; even though Jewish men were supposed to visit the Temple for three festivals a year, few from the village could even afford to go once.

For Mary this was a special Passover. Her third son, Judas, was about to leave his childhood behind him and become a young man, a son of the Law. In the years since the death of Joseph, she'd not only been a mother but, with the help of her eldest son, a father as well. As women could also go on the pilgrimage, she was going with Jesus and Judas. She'd asked her friends, Mary and Clopas to help her second son, James. He was going to take charge while she was away. 'I don't want to leave him responsible on his own for a couple of weeks.'

Most of the pilgrims were on foot but Mary rode the family's donkey. When the caravan was complete and everyone had agreed on the first night's stopping place, they set off. Nazareth was quiet again.

A few days later the caravan reached Jerusalem. They agreed the time and place when they would meet for the return home and Judas noticed that Mary looked at Jesus and shook her head, as if remembering. His brother looked contrite. Then the whole party separated.

Jerusalem was crammed with folk and the noise of a dozen different languages made Jesus think of the story of Babel. Pilgrims had travelled from most of the countries of the eastern Mediterranean, as well as from Galilee and other nearby provinces.

Jesus was a countryman at heart and the stink of the crowded city was overwhelming – the sweat of the bodies and the filth from the animals.

Everywhere someone was selling trinkets, pots and even birds – 'Cheaper here than in the Temple!' There were sellers of food and drink, and he was shocked to hear hucksters profaning God's Word with their shouts of 'Come for water, all who're thirsty, come buy wine and milk'. If the barber, with his love of the prophet Isaiah, had heard that, he'd be very upset. Even so, some of the fried fish smelled very tasty and Jesus was tempted. Quickly he made his way to the beloved Temple, where he'd realised that God was like a father. As he squeezed through the crowd he remembered how, on that first visit, his greatest pleasure had been to sit at the feet of the Teachers. He thought of how he listened as they answered questions and engaged in deep discussions. Now he was embarrassed to bring to mind the twelve year old lad, who'd eagerly interrupted and argued.

He'd arranged to meet his relative, John, in the Temple's outer court. But it was so large; you could fit the whole of Nazareth into it. As his father was one of the Temple's priests, John knew his way around and soon spotted Jesus. They greeted each other and began to exchange news of their families. Looking around Jesus said, 'Where can we pray? It's impossible in this hubbub'. Then he saw the tethered oxen, the penned sheep and the caged pigeons. Previously, he'd gone straight to listen to the Teachers. But now he was older, he was more sensitive. 'This is a cattle market not a house of prayer'.

'You haven't seen it all yet', and John pointed him in the direction of the money-changers. 'You get used to it. At least you know that the animals sold here for the sacrifice are clean'. Jesus had brought a half shekel to pay his tax for the upkeep of the Temple. 'It's easy for you', said John. 'Galilean coins don't have images on them. That's why other folk have to change their coins – the priests won't accept the ones showing the heads of kings.'

In the crowd's ebb and flow, Jesus hung on to John. 'I feel like the prophet Amos, when he left his sheep and came out of the woods to the shrine at Bethel. I'm in a different world.'

'I suppose I'm more used to it than you but this isn't the worst. The priests, the Sadducees, who run the Temple, – not the working priests, like my father – they take commission from the money-changing, and on the profits from selling the animals.'

'And selling the pigeons' said Jesus. 'Don't forget the pigeons – those are all the poor can afford for their offering.' Jesus could feel the anger boiling up inside. 'If they're profiting from the poor, then I was right to remember Amos. He hated this kind of….corruption. God wants justice and integrity.' He exploded with rage. 'Let's go and knock over the tables and drive out the animals and set the birds free.' He began to shout 'This is God's house; it doesn't belong to the Sadducees'.

'Slow down', muttered John, holding on to him. 'You'll end up in prison. What would my mother say then?' He smiled, 'I know what Mary would say! D'you see the tower? That's where the Romans keep watch in case of trouble. They'd soon give you a whipping.' He looked round. 'Be careful, somewhere there'll be the Temple police as well.'

At the end of the week, the caravan set off on the return journey to Nazareth. They were all excited by what they'd seen and heard. But Jesus, as later he told the barber, had changed. 'I understand now why Mary often says that God cares for the hungry and rejects the rich. I also realised that the outer court is for Gentiles to worship. Y'know, loving God is for everyone. That's what Isaiah meant when he said "My house will be called a house of prayer for all nations". '

# The Patient Father

He was good at shearing his sheep. That day his arm and the shears worked as one. First there were the snips around the delicate parts, the ears, the soft belly and the tail. Then he began the firm rhythmic cuts, lifting the fleece from the sides and back. By the end of the day, he was tired. Now he'd spend the night with the flock. His friend, Jesus, hadn't yet finished the new gate so he'd lie across the door to the fold, keeping the sheep in and the wolves out. As he lay there, he started to count the flickering lights above, remembering how God had said to Abram, 'Look up at the sky and count the stars, if you can'. He chuckled at that. So God does have a sense of humour. He said his prayers and finished with one of his favourite psalms: 'Praise the Lord…who heals the broken in spirit and binds up their wounds, who numbers the stars one by one and calls each by name.' Then he thought, 'It's funny that some folk count sheep to help them sleep. Not shepherds, we have enough of that by day. No, we count the stars', and so he started, 'One, two, three…..' until his eyes closed and he slept.

In the morning he was shaken awake by the lad who watched the sheep grazing during the day. He washed in the stream, had a bite of bread and cheese and then went off to join the old men who sat in the shade under the ancient olive tree.

When the barber appeared, they all livened up and the old farmer, Alpheus, called out, 'Have you brought your shears – and I don't mean those greasy ones you use on the sheep.'

He waved the small ones in reply, 'Never without them.' So Alpheus sat on the tree stump and the barber began to cut his hair. 'How are the boys?' he asked.

'Aye', asked one of the watching men, 'What's James been up to lately? He's a fine lad, your eldest, a good worker on the farm as well as putting these Romans in their place.' James was a patriot, perhaps even a Zealot, one of the Jewish guerrillas trying to make things difficult for the occupying Romans.

'Sshhh', several men hushed the loudmouth.

The barber looked round, 'Less of that dangerous talk. If word gets around, they'll nail him to a cross.'

But Old Grumpy couldn't keep quiet and joined in. 'Better a dishonourable death than having your brain-box son collecting taxes. It's bad enough being overrun by foreigners, without having to pay for the privilege. Pfff – Levi!' He spat on the ground and the others nodded and muttered their agreement. He went on, 'If you spoke the truth, Alpheus, you'd admit it would have been better if he'd herded filthy pigs.'

The barber stopped cutting and tapped his shears on the

comb, 'I'll say this for Levi, young Jesus thinks he's alright and that one day he'll come to his senses and return home.'

'That's right', said Alpheus, 'I'm glad they're still friends. Jesus is always telling me to be patient. "A good father with a wayward child" he says, "is just like God is with us. He loves us all, with all our faults and failures and waits for us to change and go back to him." '

The barber returned to his cutting and, nodding over his shoulder, said, 'Jesus can't believe there's any hope for this bunch of reprobates.'

'All the same, I'll bet your James doesn't agree with all that pious nonsense', said another.

Alpheus reddened and stood up, 'I asked Jesus about that and d'you know what he said? "One day those two brothers will be pals again. And the sign will be you saying grace, when they eat together at the family table." ' He sat down again on the tree stump.

The barber remembered his psalm from the previous night and said softly, ' "How good it is to sing praises to God....who heals the broken in spirit and binds up their wounds." ' Then he took his cloth and gently wiped the loose hairs from the old man's face, deftly drying his wet eyes.

# Dirty Washing

The old men were sitting in the sun under the ancient olive tree, not far from the cisterns where the village stored its water. Nazareth had only one spring and so, over the years, a few cisterns had been dug. One was used by the animals but, naturally, the women preferred a different one for washing clothes. Most days, except on the Sabbath, women would be there. At first there wouldn't be much talking. Clothes had to be rinsed in the water and then beaten clean on the stones. But after laying them out to dry in the sunshine, they'd time to talk. They were altogether different from the old men in their parliament. All ages were here, from young children with their mothers to bent elderly widows and not all of them were Jewish.

On that particular day the old men were bored. The winter was over; the air was still and the heat was building up. The barber was cutting one of the men's hair but, unusually, there was no conversation drowning the noise of his clipping. A couple of them were so sluggish they'd fallen asleep. Old Grumpy glanced idly up the road and then sat upright. He didn't see so well these days but it was a strange sight. Coming towards the cistern, was a woman with, alongside her, what seemed to be a walking bundle of heavy robes. What was really odd was that the bundle appeared to have the legs of a man. 'Now there's a sight I thought I'd never see: a man going to the cistern to do the washing.'

At this, the barber stopped cutting, the grey heads turned and even the sleepers awoke. It wasn't only that laundering was thought to be women's work. There were strict religious laws about cleanliness. A man handling bedclothes could easily be tainted.

'It's Mary, Joseph's widow', said Clopas. 'But who's the man? He should be ashamed touching dirty clothes. And those are heavy winter cloaks, so they'll have been used as blankets on cold nights. They'll not just be dirty, they'll be unclean. He's breaking the law of Leviticus.'

'It's only Jesus,' said the barber. This produced a chorus of disapproving chin-wagging. 'He can be a very peculiar young man, that one.'

'That's as maybe but Jesus knows what he's doing. A free haircut all round if it doesn't turn out that the laws of cleanliness can be eased to allow a young man to carry a woman's dirty washing. He's not breaking the law; he's loving his mother.'

As mother and son passed the muttering, grumbling old men, Mary said to Jesus, 'You take after your father. When we married, I was young and strong but Joseph was always ready to help with the heavy work.'

'I know that, and he wasn't just a good husband. He was

a good father as well. It's because of him that I always think God's like a good father to us.'

Mary looked at him, 'I hope you've also learned that God's like a good mother.'

He laughed. 'Of course God's like a mother. I used to watch you when we were small and went to Synagogue. I'd think you were like a hen with all her brood under her wings. And I thought then, God's like that.'

Mary smiled and punched him playfully on his arm. 'Now put those coats down and get off with you. We women'll get on with our work and you should get back to yours.'

When Jesus had gone, the women crowded round Mary to ask why her son was touching what was unclean. 'It's just that I thought it was a good day for a spring clean and so I set the girls on giving the house a good scrub. Then I collected all the cloaks that had kept us warm on cold days and were wrapped round us at night. But the girls sent for Jesus because they said they were too heavy for me to carry. I knew that Naomi and Miriam expected him to say that they had to help me instead of cleaning. But he knew. He smiled at them, nodding towards the brushes outside the house. Then he just picked up all the cloaks and set off. He's a good son, the best.'

The women told their men-folk, who told the old men, who told the barber that he didn't owe any of them free haircuts.

# The Two Kingdoms

Alphaeus and his elder son, James, climbed the rocky path from their farm in the valley. Ahead of them on the hillside was a tracery of paths linking the Nazareth houses. The old farmer was quite breathless when he reached the village's ancient olive tree. 'I'm ready for a rest', he puffed. James didn't mind. He was a local hero to the old men and they always made a fuss of him. Although he didn't talk about it, they thought he belonged to the Zealots. These were some peasants and small farmers who hated King Herod's family for being vassals of the Romans. They used guerrilla tactics to make nuisances of themselves. But their real aim was to grow strong enough to set their nation free from kings. Recruitment in recent years had become easier because Herod Antipas, who ruled Galilee on behalf of the Roman Emperor, was sucking the people dry by his demands.

When Old Grumpy saw James, he couldn't resist having a dig at Alphaeus. 'I see you've brought the good lad and not your smart-alec son.' James' brother, Levi, had disgraced his own family by serving Herod Antipas, as a tax collector.

The barber was always edgy when the conversation turned to politics, not because he didn't have strong views but he never knew who would be listening. Herod's spies were everywhere and he didn't want to be blamed because a foolish old man opened his mouth too widely. So he was relieved to see Jesus, with his loaded donkey, going past on his way to work on a house he was repairing. He played the innocent, 'Jesus, your friend James is here.' Jesus' friend was actually the other brother, Levi.

Jesus politely greeted everyone but James responded rather rudely, 'Still paying your taxes to the Romans?'

'If we want Roman roads, we must pay Roman taxes.' But he couldn't resist adding, 'What about God's taxes. Are you still paying your dues, James?'

James became belligerent. 'I pay our family's share for the synagogue and we never miss the Temple tax. Not everyone can say that.' He looked round at the circle of men.

'You don't fool God by only paying what's due. God's more concerned about the poor and the word is that some of you farmers aren't paying proper wages to your labourers.' He turned to the barber, 'Remind us what your favourite prophet would have to say about that.'

The barber sighed; his strategy to avoid politics had backfired. Like a shepherd tickling a sheep under its chin, to persuade it to move along with the flock, Jesus knew how to involve him in an argument. 'Isaiah', he replied 'teaches that true piety when you fast, is not to keep your men hard at work.' Then, in his best preaching voice he quoted the prophet: "Is not this the fast I require: to loose the fetters of injustice...sharing your food with the hungry, taking the homeless poor into your house.....and never evading a duty to your kinsfolk" '. And then twisting the knife, he turned to James, 'Such as your brother Levi!'

James hurriedly switched his argument. 'If it wasn't for the greed of the rich landowners, small farmers like us'd be able to pay fairer wages. We don't like Kings and their greedy and dissolute ways; living off our backs. We all know about Herod Antipas and his women. He's as bad as his father, Herod the Great. D'you know the latest…..'

'….. Ah, now I agree with you', interrupted Jesus, 'we're all God's children and we don't need an earthly king. In God's Kingdom, there aren't rich and poor, just one family. Each of us will care for the other and all will feed the hungry and welcome the stranger. Like the manna from heaven, God'll give us all our bread each day.'

The old men had chuckled contentedly when the two young men had argued like fighting cocks. But now that they were in agreement, they were disappointed.

Alphaeus stood up. 'Right James, I've got my breath back, we can be on our way. But I'll just say this. I won't be truly content until Levi comes home and the three of us can invite Jesus round for supper. And then, we'll all be happy.'

Jesus' donkey had found a patch of tasty fresh grass and so was as disappointed as the old men when Jesus pulled on the reins, 'Time to get back to work.' He turned to James and his father, 'Let's make a promise that one day, we'll make that happen. Then, it won't just be us who'll be happy; God and all the angels in heaven will join our celebrations.'

# A Life in Wood

It was one of those days. The carpenter was sitting on the ground using his bow drill to make a hole in a piece of wood and, suddenly, the drill slipped and the wood split. He'd no more cedar and the Teacher had been quite clear that the gift he was making to his wife had to be the best. Jesus sighed. He couldn't even begin the tricky job that his mother wanted him to do for her friend's husband, Clopas. He needed a wooden saddle for a new donkey. But before Jesus could start, he needed to feel and measure the animal's back.

He stood up and stretched, looking round at the hills, 'My help is from the Lord'. He'd made up his mind. 'James', he shouted to his brother, 'I need some peace. I'm off to see the barber.'

As he picked his way up the rough stony path, he searched for the words that would explain his feelings. The barber was a good listener but Jesus began to realise that his worries went deeper than split wood and donkey saddles. He saw him sat on a small knoll watching his flock crop the thin grass.

'Just in time,' he said as his young friend approached. 'I've more bread and cheese than I need.'

'Ah, remember God's gift of manna. You should take only enough for the day.'

Tearing the loaf in half, the barber held out the piece, 'Perhaps the Lord knew I'd have a visitor.'

Jesus looked at it, 'Didn't the Lord say anything about cheese? '

The barber passed over a piece, 'From my own sheep's milk.' He looked at the surrounding hills and at the valley below. 'It always reminds me of Isaiah. "Let every valley be raised, every mountain and hill be brought low....then will the glory of the Lord be revealed" '.

'When I'm on the hills', said Jesus, 'I think of Moses seeing God face to face; and Elijah hiding under a broom bush and the Lord sending him bread and water'.

They sat together, silently eating and drinking water from the shepherd's skin bag. The munching sheep ignored them. Hesitantly Jesus began, 'I've begun to think about what I should do next. Does God want me to be a carpenter all my days? So far, I've spent half my years as a child, growing and learning, mostly from my mother, about God's ways. At bedtime, she told us stories from our histories and helped me learn the Psalms. Did you know that her favourite prophet was Amos? She was always reminding us of the needs of the poor and the greed of the rich; how God cared for the humble and pulled down the powerful from their thrones.'

'And Joseph?'

'Yes, I learned from him as well. He knew how to look after his family. And he taught me all about wood, "God's gold", he called it. He loved wood. He used to laugh at himself. "I can't see the trees for the wood", he'd say. I remember my mother telling me that when I was born he made a new manger to hold the animals' feed and he laid me in it to sleep. I can still remember playing with a small bird he'd carved out of olive wood. Every time there was a new baby, it was passed on. Miriam still has it. He taught me all I know about wood: yokes for oxen, saddles for donkeys, boxes for clothes and then everything to do with boat and house building. When I think of it, from the manger to this moment, I've spent a life in wood. But he also made sure I grew up as a good Jew, taking me to the Temple for my bar mitzvah. That's when I began the second part of my life. When he died, I could see that what my mother taught, she believed. She really did trust our Father in heaven.'

'You're right. Mary's a good woman.'

'Since then I've had to be the main breadwinner and help her care for the family. But is it now the time to hand over this responsibility to James? I won't be here always. I need to know how best to use the gifts God's given me. Look around; there are so many sick, hungry and powerless people in Galilee. Should I be a healer, like you; or bake bread for the hungry or become a Zealot and lead people to fight against greedy, faithless rulers?

The barber shook his head. 'I've no idea. Though when you sit on the tree stump for me to cut your hair, I look at you and I remember Isaiah's words: "A shoot shall come out of the stump of Jesse….the spirit of the Lord shall rest on him, the spirit of wisdom and understanding." And I say to myself, that's you, my lad, that's you.'

The boy who helped look after the sheep came and so the young man and his old friend walked together back to Nazareth. 'What now?' asked Jesus.

'That's obvious,' replied the barber. 'You've to finish those jobs promised to the Teacher and to Clopas – they're God's work too.'

'Yes and all the old chaps will be waiting in the shade of the ancient olive tree for you to smarten their beards.' He smiled, 'Serving God takes us down some very strange paths.'

But when they reached the ancient tree, it was late and the old men weren't waiting. They'd gone home to eat. Jesus went over to the tree and looked up at the tangled swaying branches. He leaned against the trunk and stroked the rough bark. 'When we were children we'd come here with Joseph and hold hands in a ring round it. The older we were, the bigger the ring. A life in wood; how will it end?'

# Biblical References

Preface
    Lk 2.41ff; 3.21; 3.23; 2.52

Number 43
    Mt 11.30; Ezek 5.1; Isa 40.11; Num 6.9; Mt 10.30;
    2 Ki 2. 23-24

Fishing for Friends
    Mk 6.3; Mk 1.16; Mt 17.24

The Miracle of Healing
    Lk 4.30; Jn 5.13; Ps 4.1 & 8 (adapted)

A Pharisee for the Synagogue
    Ex 2.1ff; Ex 7.8–9.11; Mt 5.15; Lk 11.5–8; Jn 19.25;
    Num 15.37-38; Ex 13.9 & 16; Isa 64.8

A Wedding at Nazareth
> Song of Songs 2.14; Mk 1.19; Jn 1.46; Mt 25.1; Isa 62.5;
> Jn 2.10

The Lost Lamb
> 1 Sam 1. 28; Mk 15.40; Lk 15.4ff; Jn 10.11

All at Sea
> Gen 1.1-2; Job 41.1ff; Ps 104.25-26; Ex 14.21-22;
> Lk 5.4-6; Jn 21.6

A Day Out
> Mk 6.3; Gen 5.24; 2 Ki 2.11; Mk 12.26-27; Mt 6.26-29

My Friend the Tax Collector
> Mk 2.14; Mt 9.9; Mk 3.18; Lk 18.3; Mt 10.3; Is 57.2;
> Mk 2.17; Mk 10.18

A Nazareth Sabbath
> Ex 20.8; Lk 14.5

To the Hills
> Isa 55.12; Mt 5.14; Lk 1.36; Jn 10.1–16; Mk 6.17ff;
> Mt 8.20; Josh 3.14ff; Mk 1.6; Ps 118.22; Mt 21.42

The Nazareth Caravan
> Deut 16.1-8; Lk 2.41-52; Isa 55.1; Ex 20.4; Mt 21.12-13;
> Jn 2.13-17; Lk 1.53; Isa 56.7

The Patient Father
    Gen 15.5; Ps 147.3-4; Lk 15.11ff

Dirty Washing
    Lev 12.1-15.33; Mt 23.37

The Two Kingdoms
    Mk 2.14; Mt 22.17ff; Isa 58.3-7; Mk 6.17ff; Mt 2.1;
    Ex 16.14ff; Mt 6.11; Lk 15.11ff; Lk 15.10 & 32

A Life in Wood
    Ps 121.1; Ex 16.14ff; Isa 40.4-5; Mt 17.3; Ex 19.3; 1Ki 19.6;
    Lk 1.52-53; Isa 11.1-2

# Acknowledgements

Preachers preparing sermons every week know better than anyone how much they owe to the scholars who have studied and taught the Bible. Storytellers also are in their debt.

In addition to writing sermons, opportunities for broadcasting, mostly on the radio, have meant that I've learned from generations of producers responsible for the BBC's religious programmes. It's now over thirty years since one of them, Celia Bonner, encouraged me to begin writing stories.

In exploring what I've described as the gap years of Jesus, I have been stimulated by the interest of Graham Cook, Alan Gaunt, Jim and Jill Hollyman, and Jack McKelvey. I am grateful to them all. I have also had particular help, creative criticism and stimulating affirmation from a friend and former colleague, Brian Baker, who would have cut those adjectives.

Finally, throughout my work as a minister, I have been

partnered by Valerie. She has been my severest critic and greatest encourager. Her careful checking of this manuscript has ensured that injudicious words, floating commas and mixed tenses have been eliminated. She's even laughed at the jokes; who could ask for anything more?